Target time: 10 minutes

↓

■ 1–3. For each of the words below, choose the correct group.
the line.

T = tree   **F** = flower

dandelion _____   pine _____   bluebell _____

oak _____   elm _____   fir _____

■ In each group, three words go together. Two words do not go with the other three. Underline the **two** words that are the **odd ones out**.

Example great   excellent   <u>awful</u>   brilliant   <u>terrible</u>

4. peaceful   noisy   quiet   silent   racket
5. eagle   parrot   cat   pigeon   rat
6. scooter   car   tricycle   bicycle   train

■ Underline the pair of words that are most **opposite** in meaning.

Example (<u>useful, useless</u>)   (fix, mend)   (broken, tool)

7. (fib, unkind)   (rude, polite)   (shove, careful)
8. (south, north)   (down, low)   (way, help)
9. (damp, ruff)   (leaf, bark)   (rough, smooth)

■ **Two** words in each sentence must change places so that the sentence makes sense. Underline the two words.

Example I am <u>sleepy</u> <u>not</u> yet.   (I am <u>not</u> <u>sleepy</u> yet.)

10. Ladybirds spots have on their backs.
11. All insects six have legs.
12. The is rain pouring down.

End of test.

Score:	Time taken:	Target met?

Section 1 Test 3

■ Underline the pair of words that mean almost the **same**.

> **Example** (oven, pan)　　(eat, cupboard)　　(cook, chef)

1. (job, profession)　　(kitten, vet)　　(basket, teacher)
2. (liquid, poison)　　(twig, hospital)　　(cure, remedy)
3. (count, amount)　　(maximum, most)　　(closet, held)

■ Choose the word that best completes the sentence. Underline the answer.

> **Example** **Snow** is to **cold** as **sunshine** is to (sky, hot, cloud).

4. **Mother** is to **father** as **sister** is to (auntie, cat, brother, annoying).
5. **School** is to **learn** as **office** is to (play, work, drive, paper).
6. **Car** is to **wheels** as **plane** is to (wings, feather, beak, swoop).

■ 7–9. Look at the groups. For each of the words below, choose the correct group.
Write its letter on the line.

> **T** = town or city　**C** = country

London _____　　France _____　　Spain _____

Paris _____　　Madrid _____　　Belgium _____

■ In each group, three words go together. Two do not go with the other three.
Underline the **two** words that are the **odd ones out**.

> **Example** great　　excellent　　awful　　brilliant　　terrible

10. circle　　diamond　　rhombus　　oval　　rectangle
11. hammer　　spatula　　fork　　ladle　　chisel
12. angry　　joyful　　sad　　pleased　　happy

End of test.

Score:		Time taken:		Target met?	

Ages 8–9

Schofield & Sims

Verbal Reasoning 3

Rapid Reasoning Tests

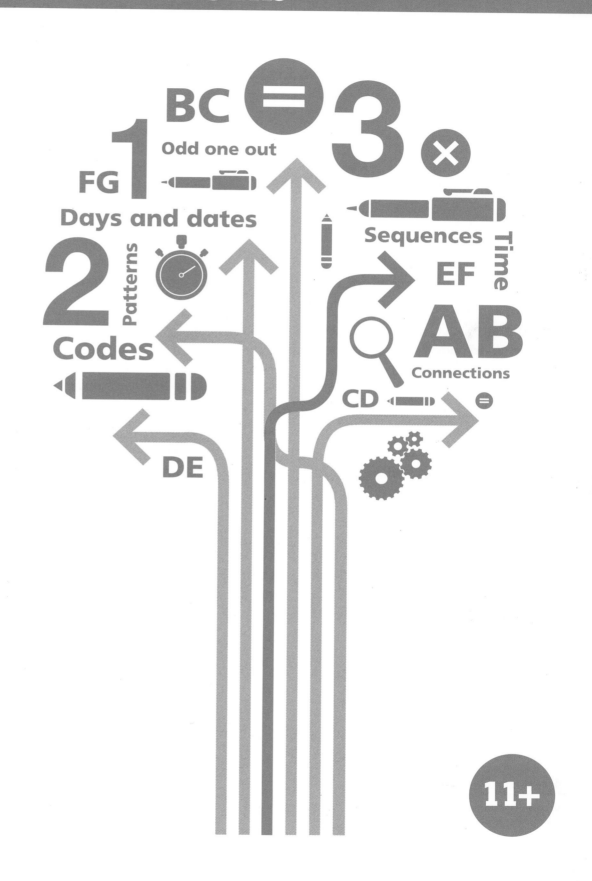

BC
Odd one out
FG 1
Days and dates
2 Patterns
Codes
DE
3 ×
Sequences   Time
EF
AB
Connections
CD

11+

Name

Introduction

The **Rapid Reasoning Tests** give you practice in answering verbal reasoning questions. The questions are like the questions in the 11+ and other school tests. You must find the correct answers.

Selection tests are usually timed, so you must also work quickly. To check how quickly you are working, you should time how long you spend on every test. Or you can ask an adult to time you.

What you need

- A pencil
- An eraser
- A sheet of rough paper
- A clock, watch or stopwatch
- An adult to mark the test for you and to help you to work out how long you take

What to do

- Turn to **Section 1 Test 1** on page 4. Look at the green box, labelled **Target time**. This tells you how long the test should take.
- When you are ready to start, write down the time or start the stopwatch. Or the adult helping you will tell you to begin.
- Find the symbol ↓ near the top of the first page. The instructions for the first set of questions are beside it. Read them carefully.
- Look at the **Example** below the instructions. Work out why the answer given is correct.
- Using similar methods, answer each question. Show your answer in the way that the answer is shown in the example. For instance, you might need to write your answer on the line or underline the correct answer from a selection given.
- Do your best. Work quickly. Try to answer every question. But if you do get stuck on a question, leave it. Go on to the next.
- Each test is one page long. When you reach the words **End of test**, stop. Write down the time or stop the stopwatch. Or tell the adult helping you that you have finished.
- With the adult, work out how long you took to do the test. Fill in the **Time taken** box.
- The adult will mark your work and fill in the **Score** and **Target met?** boxes.
- Always have another go at questions that you got wrong. Try again without looking at the answers.
- Later you will do some more tests. You will soon learn to find the correct answers more quickly. The adult who is helping you will tell you what to do next.

Published by Schofield & Sims Ltd,
Dogley Mill, Fenay Bridge, Huddersfield HD8 0NQ, UK
Telephone 01484 607080
www.schofieldandsims.co.uk

Copyright © Schofield & Sims Ltd, 2014

Author: **Siân Goodspeed**. Siân Goodspeed has asserted her moral right under the Copyright, Designs and Patents Act, 1988, to be identified as the author of this work.

British Library Cataloguing in Publication Data. A catalogue record for this book is available from the British Library.

Commissioned by **Carolyn Richardson Publishing Services** (www.publiserve.co.uk)

Design by **Oxford Designers & Illustrators**
Front cover design by **Ledgard Jepson Ltd**
Printed in India by **Multivista Global Ltd**

ISBN 978 07217 1240 6

Contents

A **pull-out answers section** (pages A1 to A8) appears in the centre of this book, between pages 20 and 21. It also gives simple guidance on how best to use this book. Remove this section before you begin working through the tests.

■ Underline the two words, **one** from each group, that mean almost the **same**.

> **Example** (oven, <u>chef</u>, cupboard)　　(eat, pan, <u>cook</u>)

1. (narrow, slim, wide)　　(broad, length, height)
2. (class, commence, date)　　(teacher, begin, fruit)
3. (raised, exceptional, born)　　(baked, rubbish, outstanding)

■ Choose the word that best completes the sentence. Underline the answer.

> **Example** **Snow** is to **cold** as **sunshine** is to (sky, <u>hot</u>, cloud).

4. **Hare** is to **fast** as **tortoise** is to (green, old, slow, last).
5. **Laugh** is to **cry** as **shout** is to (talk, yell, whisper, angry).
6. **Spin** is to **pin** as **twin** is to (won, own, tin, win).

■ Underline the two words, **one** from each group, that are most **opposite** in meaning.

> **Example** (<u>useless</u>, broken, mend)　　(<u>useful</u>, fix, tool)

7. (deep, wet, cold)　　(shallow, new, calm)
8. (win, top, special)　　(loose, dear, lose)
9. (dog, live, care)　　(die, ill, bird)

■ Underline the word that goes best with the three words in brackets.

> **Example** (fork, teaspoon, knife)　　plate, glass, <u>spoon</u>

10. (dog, cat, hamster)　　rabbit, dinosaur, hawk
11. (ruler, pencil, notebook)　　knife, king, pen
12. (magazine, newspaper, leaflet)　　shelf, radio, book

End of test

Score:	Time taken:	Target met?

Target time: **10 minutes**

■ Add a letter to each word to make a new word. Use the same letter for each pair of words, and put it in the same place in each. Write the new words on the lines. Choose your answer from the following letters: **a e t l k y**

Example bun, pea ___bunk___ , ___peak___ (add **k** to the end of each word)

1. trip, grip _____ , _____

2. ever, hone _____ , _____

3. amp, oaf _____ , _____

■ In each of the sentences below, the word in capitals has three letters missing. Those three letters spell a word. Write the three-letter word in the gap.

Example I helped my sister tie up her shoe L A C E S.

4. The girl S __ __ __ P E D with her rope across the playground.

5. My little sister likes to play on the S __ __ __ E.

6. What is today's D __ __ __ ?

■ Find the missing letter that completes **both** pairs of words. Write the letter on the lines. Choose your answer from the following letters: **d p n e r t**

Example kil [t] oll   ten [t] old   (kilt and toll, tent and told)

7. soun [__] rill   dea [__] ream

8. skat [__] asy   plac [__] ver

9. jum [__] urse   cam [__] ray

■ If these words were listed in alphabetical order, which word would come **third**? Write the answer on the line.

Example lot   many   few   load   too ___load___

10. cheese   banana   carrot   biscuit   apple _____

11. circle   square   rectangle   star   rhombus _____

12. above   under   around   over   between _____

End of test.

Score:		Time taken:		Target met?	

Target time: 10 minutes

↓
■ Find the missing letter that completes **both** pairs of words. Write the letter on the lines. Choose your answer from the following letters: **r l e t w y**

| **Example** kil [_t_] oll   ten [_t_] old   (kilt and toll, tent and told) |

1. maz [___] rupt   jok [___] rase
2. stra [___] eak   kno [___] est
3. lowe [___] eply   mothe [___] escue

- - -

■ Find the **four-letter word** hidden across two or more consecutive words in each sentence below. The order of the letters must stay the same. Underline the word and write it on the line.

| **Example** My tea made me ill.   _____team_____ |

4. Lions and tigers are fierce. _____
5. I like fish fingers for tea. _____
6. How is her father? _____

- - -

■ Underline the two words that contain all the same letters.

| **Example** bake   cake   bird   beak   rake |

7. sage   saga   ages   gaps   spar
8. drip   wind   ward   draw   wren
9. dear   rain   read   raid   deal

- - -

■ Underline the two words, **one** from each group, that together make one new word. The word from the first group comes first.

| **Example** (clock, watch, week)   (time, work, stop)   (clockwork) |

10. (screen, radio, mouse)   (sound, saver, poison)
11. (head, foot, leg)   (set, show, trousers)
12. (care, wash, brush)   (more, less, wish)

End of test

| Score: | | Time taken: | | Target met? | |

Target time: **10 minutes**

Change the first word into the last word. Only change one letter at a time. You must make a new word in the middle. Write the new word on the line.

Example MILK [__MILE__] TILE

1. LIMP [_____] MIME
2. WEAR [_____] TEAM
3. RIDE [_____] PIPE

In each of the sentences below, the word in capitals has three letters missing. Those three letters spell a word. Write the three-letter word in the gap.

Example I helped my sister tie up her shoe L A C E S.

4. The woman was S __ __ __ ED of the mouse.
5. The girl loved C __ __ __ ING in her tent.
6. The noise was loud and S U D __ __ __ .

Underline the two words, **one** from each group, that together make one new word. The word from the first group comes first.

Example (clock, watch, week)   (time, work, stop)   (clockwork)

7. (bit, bite, bank)   (food, ten, tan)
8. (soil, worm, earth)   (quake, fear, scared)
9. (snow, ice, cold)   (board, ski, silk)

If these words were listed in alphabetical order, which word would come **fourth**? Write the answer on the line.

Example lot   many   few   load   too   ___many___

10. number   letter   paper   pencil   time   _____
11. run   walk   jog   sprint   jump   _____
12. kind   polite   cruel   perfect   keen   _____

End of test.

Score:		Time taken:		Target met?	

⬇
■ Find the next number in the sequence. Write it on the line.

> **Example** 6   9   12   15   18   __21__   (+3 each time)

1. 12   14   16   18   20   _____
2. 11   9   7   5   3   _____
3. 3   8   13   18   23   _____

■ Use the information given to answer the sum. Write your answer as a **letter**.

> **Example** A = 1   B = 2   C = 3   D = 5   E = 8   **A + B + D =** __E__   (1 + 2 + 5 = 8)

4. A = 2   B = 6   C = 3   D = 9   E = 20   **B × C + A =** _____
5. A = 15   B = 5   C = 26   D = 4   E = 7   **E + D + A =** _____
6. A = 3   B = 11   C = 90   D = 10   E = 107   **B × D − A =** _____

■ Work out the missing number. Write it on the line.

> **Example** 3 [9] 3   4 [8] 2   5 [__15__] 3
> (a × b = ?, where a represents the number on the left and b represents the number on the right)

7. 13 [39] 3   0 [0] 24   6 [_____] 0
8. 40 [45] 5   30 [38] 8   9 [_____] 30
9. 1 [56] 56   9 [72] 8   12 [_____] 6

■ Find the missing number in each equation. Write it on the line.

> **Example** 10 − 3 = 2 + __5__   (10 − 3 = 7 and so does 2 + 5)

10. 20 + 6 = 20 + 4 + _____
11. 15 ÷ 3 = 3 + _____
12. 100 ÷ 10 = 15 − 4 − _____

End of test

Score:		Time taken:		Target met?	

Target time: **10 minutes**

■ Work out the missing number. Write it on the line.

Example 3 [9] 3 4 [8] 2 5 [___15___] 3

($a \times b = ?$, where a represents the number on the left and b represents the number on the right)

1. 25 [75] 3 2 [4] 2 12 [_____] 3
2. 27 [60] 33 17 [31] 14 18 [_____] 19
3. 40 [4] 36 50 [25] 25 70 [_____] 12

■ Find the missing number in each equation. Write it on the line.

Example 10 – 3 = 2 + ___5___ (10 – 3 = 7 and so does 2 + 5)

4. 66 + 4 = 10 × _____
5. 21 + 3 = 20 + _____
6. 71 – 1 = 7 × _____

■ Find the next number in the sequence. Write it on the line.

Example 6 9 12 15 18 ___21___ (+3 each time)

7. 23 20 17 14 11 _____
8. 160 80 40 20 10 _____
9. 12 15 18 21 24 _____

■ Use the information given to answer the sum. Write your answer as a **letter**.

Example A = 1 B = 2 C = 3 D = 5 E = 8 **A + B + D =** ___E___ (1 + 2 + 5 = 8)

10. A = 5 B = 115 C = 10 D = 120 E = 145 **D + A – C =** _____
11. A = 35 B = 3 C = 8 D = 4 E = 32 **C × D + B =** _____
12. A = 12 B = 0 C = 48 D = 2 E = 4 **C ÷ E – A =** _____

End of test.

Score:		Time taken:		Target met?	

Target time: **10 minutes**

➜
■ Find the next letter pair in the sequence. Use the alphabet to help you. Write your answer on the line.

A B C D E F G H I J K L M N O P Q R S T U V W X Y Z

Example AD	BE	CF	DG	EH	FI	(+1, +1)

1. XZ   YY   ZX   AW   _____
2. CC   BC   AC   ZC   _____
3. WB   YD   AF   CH   _____

■ Find the letter pair that completes each sentence. Use the alphabet to help you. Write your answer on the line.

A B C D E F G H I J K L M N O P Q R S T U V W X Y Z

Example **FP** is to **JT** as **AA** is to _EE_ .	(+4, +4)

4. **LM** is to **PQ** as **ST** is to _____ .
5. **DL** is to **FN** as **RT** is to _____ .
6. **FM** is to **IP** as **MO** is to _____ .

■ Make a new word by changing the third pair in the same way as the other pairs. Write the new word on the line.

Example (snip, nip) (slit, lit) (then, ___hen___)	(take away the first letter of the first word

7. (white, with)   (weird, wire)   (speed, _____)
8. (merit, tire)   (trees, seer)   (petal, _____)
9. (cream, mare)   (pleat, tale)   (paler, _____)

■ Match the number codes to the words. Use this to help you work out the answers to the questions. Write your answers on the lines.

BOX   TOP   APE   BAT   129   148   435   823

10. What is the code for **POT**? _____
11. What is the code for **BOAT**? _____
12. What does the code **8435** mean? _____

End of test

Score:	Time taken:	Target met?

Target time: 10 minutes

■ Crack the code. Use the alphabet to help you. Write your answer on the line.

A B C D E F G H I J K L M N O P Q R S T U V W X Y Z

Example If the code for **SING** is **TJOH**, what is the code for **LONG**? ___MPOH___

(+1 from the word to the code each time)

1. If the code for **SHOW** is **TIPX**, what is the code for **EAT**? _____
2. If the code for **CURE** is **DVSF**, what is the code for **RED**? _____
3. If the code for **HORSE** is **IPSTF**, what is the code for **CAT**? _____

■ Match the number codes to the words. Use this to help you work out the answers to the questions. Write your answers on the lines.

AXE   FAR   NOT   RAT   194   513   312   672

4. What is the code for **FOX**? _____
5. What is the code for **OAT**? _____
6. What does the code **5772** mean? _____

■ The word in square brackets has been made by some of the letters from the two outside words. Make a new word in the middle of the second group of words in the same way. Write the new word on the line.

Example (each [east] slot)   (half [___hare___] rope)

7. (stub [turn] rein)   (smog [_____] pace)
8. (farm [frog] ogle)   (sows [_____] anew)
9. (dupe [pulp] loop)   (disc [_____] look)

■ Find the next letter pair in the sequence. Use the alphabet to help you. Write your answer on the line.

A B C D E F G H I J K L M N O P Q R S T U V W X Y Z

Example AD   BE   CF   DG   EH   ___FI___   (+1, +1)

10. YK YK ZL ZL AM _____
11. BD AC ZB YA _____
12. PL UG ZB EW _____

End of test.

Score:		Time taken:		Target met?	

Target time: **10 minutes**

↓ ■ Read the following information. Work out the answers. Write your answers on the lines.

1. Three people are queuing for train tickets. Beth is at the front of the line. Simon is two places behind her. Gemma is standing in front of Simon. Who is at the back? _____

2. Four horses are racing. Sprint is coming third, in between Trot and Gallop. Trot is behind Shiver. Who is winning the race? _____

3. Four friends line up from youngest to oldest. Shappy is at the front of the line. Sonia is standing behind her. Oliver is the oldest of the friends. Sam is standing behind Sonia. Who is last in the line? _____

■ Circle the letter next to the **true** statement for each question.

4. Biscuits are made with flour, butter and sugar. Sugar tastes very sweet.

   If the above statements are true, which one of the following statements must also be true?
   A. Birthday cakes have candles on them.
   B. Biscuits taste sweet.
   C. Biscuits are baked in a hot oven.
   D. Sugar is bad for your teeth.

5. Woodwind instruments need air to make a sound. Flutes are woodwind instruments.

   If the above statements are true, which one of the following statements must also be true?
   A. Guitars have strings.
   B. Flutes need air blown into them to make a sound.
   C. All woodwind instruments are flutes.
   D. Piano players are good at music.

■ Read the following information. Work out the answers. Write your answers on the lines.

6. Holly is 2 years older than Molly. Molly is 9. How old is Holly? _____

7. Lara's friend, Beata, is 3 years older than her. If Lara is 13, how old is Beata? _____

8. Pete and Milo were born 3 days apart. If Milo was born first, on 16 July, when was Pete born? _____

9. Theresa is going to the zoo the day after tomorrow. If today is Friday, when will Theresa go to the zoo? _____

10. Meg is going ice-skating the day after tomorrow. If today is Wednesday, when is Meg going ice-skating? _____

11. Sara went to the park yesterday. If today is Sunday, when did Sara go to the park? _____

12. Which month comes 2 months after March? _____

End of test

Score:		Time taken:		Target met?	

Target time: 10 minutes

⬇ Circle the letter next to the **true** statement for each question.

1. Faiza is making a gingerbread house with her friend. Faiza has **10** sweets and her friend has **12** sweets.

   If the above statements are true, which one of the following statements must also be true?
   A. The gingerbread house has windows.
   B. Faiza has fewer sweets than her friend.
   C. Faiza's father likes gingerbread.
   D. Faiza wants to live in the gingerbread house.

2. Bees can see all colours except the colour red. A honeybee is a type of bee.

   If the above statements are true, which one of the following statements must also be true?
   A. Bees make honey.
   B. Bees pollinate flowers.
   C. Bees live in beehives.
   D. Honeybees cannot see the colour red.

■ Read the following information. Work out the answers. Write your answers on the lines.

3. Jill needs to move **36** books to another room. She can carry **4** books at a time. How many trips will she need to make to move all the books? _____

4. Sam is listening to the radio. The radio show he likes to listen to is half an hour long. It starts at **4.30** p.m. What time will the radio show end? _____

5. Raj has **20** pairs of socks. **6** pairs are green, **5** pairs are blue and **7** pairs are red. The rest are yellow. How many pairs of yellow socks does Raj have? _____

6. Jason starts his homework at **5.15** p.m. It takes him **45** minutes to complete his science project and **35** minutes to finish his artwork. At what time does Jason finish all his homework? _____

7. Frieda leaves for work at **8.35** a.m. She arrives at her office at **9.15** a.m. How long did it take Frieda to travel to work? _____

8. It takes Mr Costa 4 and a half hours to drive to Plymouth. He arrives at **3.30** p.m. What time did he set off? _____

9. Becky starts getting ready for school at **7.40** a.m. She has a 10-minute shower and then spends 15 minutes getting dressed. By what time is she showered and dressed? _____

10. One turn on the fast roundabout lasts **5** minutes. Jake has three turns in a row. If his first turn starts at **2.10** p.m., what time will he get off the roundabout? _____

11. Bella usually leaves for work at **1.55** p.m. Today she is running **20** minutes late. What time will she leave for work? _____

12. Zara spends **2** hours riding her horse and then **1** hour grooming him. She finishes grooming her horse at **5.00** p.m. What time did she start riding? _____

End of test.

Score:	Time taken:	Target met?

⬇
■ Read the following information. Work out the answers. Write your answers on the lines.

1. Billy collects beetles. He has **3** shiny green beetles and **2** blue beetles. His favourite colour is red and he only has **1** beetle that is this colour. How many beetles does Billy have? _____

2. Yasmin and Gina are taking part in their school sports day. Yasmin competes in the long jump and javelin throw. Gina runs the relay race and hurts her ankle during the race. How many activities did the girls take part in between them? _____

3. Leila's mother is serving dinner. There are **10** potatoes to share between **3** people. Everyone has the same number of potatoes except for Leila's father who gets an extra one. How many potatoes does her father get? _____

■ Circle the letter next to the **true** statement for each question.

4. People who can play instruments are called musicians. Tommy plays guitar in a band.

   If the above statements are true, which one of the following statements must also be true?
   A. Tommy's band is very popular.
   B. Tommy makes lots of money.
   C. Tommy is a musician.
   D. Tommy's parents think he makes too much noise.

5. James' favourite colour is green. All of his schoolbooks are his favourite colour.

   If the above statements are true, which one of the following statements must also be true?
   A. James dislikes school.
   B. James' schoolbooks are green.
   C. His maths book is red.
   D. James has **10** schoolbooks.

■ Read the following information. Work out the answers. Write your answers on the lines.

6. Which month is **2** months before June? _____

7. If it is December now, what was the month before last? _____

8. If Tom is **2** years older than Jana and Jana is **8**, how old is Tom? _____

9. Freya is cleaning. It takes her **20** minutes to wash the dishes and **35** minutes to scrub the floor. Freya starts cleaning at **1.15 p.m.** What time does she finish? _____

10. How many days are there in August? _____

11. If it is **21** February today, what date will it be tomorrow? _____

12. One day it takes Clio **45** minutes to get to school. It takes twice as long for her to get home after school. How long does it take her to get home? _____

End of test

Score:		Time taken:		Target met?	

Target time: 10 minutes

■ Underline the word in brackets that is **closest** in meaning to the word in capitals.

Example CHEF (kitchen, <u>cook</u>, eat, oven, pan)

1. HOLD   (label, hand, grasp, level, open)
2. GUESS   (wink, sniff, peek, reply, estimate)
3. HURT   (please, harm, lope, question, ask)
4. DENY   (shake, agree, reply, refuse, still)

■ Choose the word that best completes the sentence. Underline the answer.

Example **Snow** is to **cold** as **sunshine** is to (sky, <u>hot</u>, cloud).

5. **Train** is to **track** as **boat** is to (sail, bank, ocean, pirate).
6. **Rabbit** is to **hutch** as **dog** is to (kennel, resort, villa, hotel).
7. **Owl** is to **night** as **robin** is to (light, midnight, day, worm).
8. **Purse** is to **money** as **fridge** is to (sweets, food, soap, freeze).

■ Underline the word in brackets that is most **opposite** in meaning to the word in capitals.

Example USEFUL   (broken, <u>useless</u>, mend, fix)

9. FROWN   (chew, smile, spit, dot, point)
10. BEAUTIFUL   (princess, ugly, feet, castle, eyes)
11. FULL   (leak, bowl, spill, empty, milk)

■ Read the following information. Work out the answer. Write your answer on the line.

12. Rob and Pat share **34** biscuits equally between them. How many biscuits do Rob and Pat get each?

_____

End of test.

Score:		Time taken:		Target met?	

Target time: **10 minutes**

1–4. Look at the words in groups A, B and C. For each of the words below, choose the correct group and write its letter on the line.

A	B	C
bicycle	van	canoe

moped _____   yacht _____   scooter _____

motorbike _____   kayak _____

truck _____   lorry _____   dinghy _____

In each group, three words go together. Two words do not go with the other three. Underline the **two** words that are the **odd ones out**.

Example great   excellent   <u>awful</u>   brilliant   <u>terrible</u>

5. turquoise   pink   red   cyan   blue
6. galaxy   Earth   sun   Venus   Saturn
7. swan   goose   duck   feathers   river
8. scowl   frown   wink   glower   grin

Underline the word that goes best with the three words in brackets.

Example (fork, teaspoon, knife)   plate, glass, <u>spoon</u>

9. (thoughtful, affectionate, caring)   polite, abrupt, sympathetic
10. (small, little, tiny)   twiddle, miniature, model
11. (plum, apple, banana)   cake, strawberry, celery

Read the following information. Work out the answer. Write your answer on the line.

12. Graham and Susie had cereal for breakfast. Susie also had toast. Sylvie and Josef only had toast for breakfast. How many people ate some toast at breakfast time? _____

End of test

Score:		Time taken:		Target met?	

Target time: **10 minutes**

■ In each group, three words go together. Two words do not go with the other three. Underline the **two** words that are the **odd ones out**.

Example great   excellent   <u>awful</u>   brilliant   <u>terrible</u>

1. forbid   outlaw   burglar   prohibit   dislike
2. fling   throw   toss   cup   jump
3. tiger   wolf   lion   puppy   cheetah
4. hip   waist   rib   waste   scarf

■ Choose the word that best completes the sentence. Underline the answer.

Example **Snow** is to **cold** as **sunshine** is to (sky, <u>hot</u>, cloud).

5. **Butterfly** is to **caterpillar** as **frog** is to (egg, tadpole, baby, pond).
6. **Sit** is to **sat** as **walk** is to (ran, walked, sprinted, tripped).
7. **Sink** is to **float** as **dangerous** is to (fire, safe, panic, hazard).
8. **Pin** is to **nip** as **bat** is to (tab, wing, tub, ball).

■ Underline the two words, **one** from each group, that mean almost the **same**.

Example (oven, <u>chef</u>, cupboard)   (eat, pan, <u>cook</u>)

9. (clasp, lift, hair)   (trim, snip, clip)
10. (elbow, model, miniature)   (bug, knee, tiny)
11. (least, last, many)   (minimum, queue, back)

■ Circle the letter next to the **true** statement.

12. Dinosaurs became extinct millions of years ago. A pterodactyl is a type of dinosaur.

If the above statements are true, which one of the following statements must also be true?
A. Dinosaurs used to eat people.
B. Pterodactyls are fierce.
C. A diplodocus is a type of dinosaur.
D. Pterodactyls are extinct.

End of test.

Score:		Time taken:		Target met?	

Take a letter away from each word to make two new words. The letter you take away should be in the same position in each word in the pair. Write the new words on the lines.

Example tray, cram _____ray_____ , _____ram_____ (remove the first letter from each word)

1. leap, roam _____ , _____

2. think, swamp _____ , _____

3. claw, band _____ , _____

4. train, peach _____ , _____

In each of the sentences below, the word in capitals has three letters missing. Those three letters spell a word. Write the three-letter word in the gap.

Example I helped my sister tie up her shoe L _A_ _C_ _E_ S.

5. She put her C __ __ __ HES in the drawer.

6. The elephant was __ __ __ E compared to the mouse.

7. The boy was told to be P O __ __ __ E to his grandmother.

8. The soup tasted H O R __ __ __ L E.

Rearrange the word in capitals. Use the letters to make another word that goes with the first two. Write the new word on the line.

Example pea grain BANE _____BEAN_____

9. light dark LEAP _____

10. fawn doe REED _____

11. ring circle POOL _____

Read the following information. Work out the answer. Write your answer on the line.

12. Four people are waiting for a bus. Shameet is at the front of the queue. Michael is two places behind Shameet. Sally is standing behind Michael. Frank is two places in front of Sally. Who is second in the queue? _____

End of test

Notes for parents, tutors, teachers and other adult helpers

- **Verbal Reasoning 3** is designed for eight- and nine-year-olds, but may also be suitable for some older children.

- Remove this pull-out section before giving the book to the child.

- Before the child begins work on the first test, read together the instructions on page 2, headed **What to do**. As you do so, look together at **Section 1 Test 1** or another of the Section 1 tests and point out to the child the different elements.

- As each question type is introduced for the first time within a particular test, an example is given. Where question types recur throughout the book, the same example is provided. This is deliberate: the example will act as a useful reminder, but children will not need to work through it repeatedly from scratch.

- Make sure that the child understands how to answer the questions and that he or she has a pencil and eraser. You should also ensure that the child is able to see a clock or a watch.

- Explain to the child how he or she should go about timing the test. Alternatively, you may wish to time the test yourself. When the child has finished the test, you should together work out the **Time taken** and complete the box that appears at the end of the test.

- Mark the child's work using this pull-out section, giving one mark for each correct answer unless instructed otherwise. Then complete the **Score** box at the end of the test.

- The table below shows you how to mark the **Target met?** box and the **Action** notes give you some guidance as you plan the next step. However, these are suggestions only. Please use your own judgement as you decide how best to proceed.

Score	Time taken	Target met?	Action
1–6	Any	Not yet	Give the child the previous book in the series. Provide help and support as needed.
7–9	Any	Not yet	Encourage the child to keep practising using the tests in this book. The child may need to repeat some tests. If so, wait a few weeks, or the child may simply remember the correct answers. Provide help and support as needed.
10–12	Over target – child took too long	Not yet	
10–12	On target – child took suggested time or less	Yes	Encourage the child to keep practising using further tests in this book, and to move on to the next book when you think this is appropriate.

- Whatever the test score, always encourage the child to have another go at the questions that he or she got wrong – without looking at the solutions. If the child's answers are still incorrect, work through these questions together. Demonstrate the correct method if necessary.

- If the child struggles with particular question types, help him or her to develop the strategies needed.

The **Understanding Reasoning** series, also available from Schofield & Sims, provides clear explanations on how to answer reasoning questions. It also provides 'Tips for tests' and 'Tips for revision'. For further details on this and other series that help children and young people to prepare for school selection tests, and for free downloads relating to the **Rapid Reasoning Tests**, visit www.schofieldandsims.co.uk

Answers

Section 1 Test 1 (page 4)

1. wide, broad
2. commence, begin
3. exceptional, outstanding
4. slow
5. whisper
6. win
7. deep, shallow
8. win, lose
9. live, die
10. rabbit
11. pen
12. book

Section 1 Test 2 (page 5)

1–3. *[score half a point for each correct answer]*
dandelion = F, pine = T, bluebell = F,
oak = T, elm = T, fir = T
4. noisy, racket (the others are calm words)
5. cat, rat (the others are all birds)
6. car, train (the others are unpowered)
7. rude, polite
8. south, north
9. rough, smooth
10. spots have (Ladybirds have spots on their backs.)
11. six have (All insects have six legs.)
12. is rain (The rain is pouring down.)

Section 1 Test 3 (page 6)

1. job, profession
2. cure, remedy
3. maximum, most
4. brother
5. work
6. wings
7–9. *[score half a point for each correct answer]*
London = T, France = C, Spain = C,
Paris = T, Madrid = T, Belgium = C
10. circle, oval (the others have 4 sides)
11. hammer, chisel (the others are kitchen utensils)
12. angry, sad (the others are happy words)

Section 1 Test 4 (page 7)

1. tripe, gripe
2. every, honey
3. lamp, loaf
4. KIP (SKIPPED)
5. LID (SLIDE)
6. ATE (DATE)
7. d (sound and drill, dead and dream)
8. e (skate and easy, place and ever)
9. p (jump and purse, camp and pray)
10. biscuit
11. rhombus
12. between

Section 1 Test 5 (page 8)

1. e (maze and erupt, joke and erase)
2. w (straw and weak, know and west)
3. r (lower and reply, mother and rescue)
4. sand (Lions and tigers are fierce.)
5. fort (I like fish fingers for tea.)
6. wish (How is her father?)
7. sage, ages
8. ward, draw
9. dear, read
10. screensaver
11. headset
12. careless

Section 1 Test 6 (page 9)

1. LIMP [LIME] MIME
2. WEAR [TEAR] TEAM
3. RIDE [RIPE] PIPE
4. CAR (SCARED)
5. AMP (CAMPING)
6. DEN (SUDDEN)
7. bitten
8. earthquake
9. snowboard
10. pencil
11. sprint
12. perfect

Section 1 Test 7 (page 10)

1. **22** (+2)
2. **1** (–2)
3. **28** (+5)
4. **E** (6 × 3 + 2 = 20)
5. **C** (7 + 4 + 15 = 26)
6. **E** (11 × 10 – 3 = 107)
7. **0** (a × b)
8. **39** (a + b)
9. **72** (a × b)
10. **2**
11. **2**
12. **1**

Section 1 Test 8 (page 11)

1. **36** (a × b)
2. **37** (a + b)
3. **58** (a – b)
4. **7**
5. **4**
6. **10**
7. **8** (–3)
8. **5** (÷2)
9. **27** (+3)
10. **B** (120 + 5 – 10 = 115)
11. **A** (8 × 4 + 3 = 35)
12. **B** (48 ÷ 4 – 12 = 0)

Section 1 Test 9 (page 12)

1. **BV** (+1, –1)
2. **YC** (–1, same)
3. **EJ** (+2, +2)
4. **WX** (+4, +4)
5. **TV** (+2, +2)
6. **PR** (+3, +3)
7. seep
8. late
9. real
10. 328
11. 1248
12. TAPE

Section 1 Test 10 (page 13)

1. **FBU** (+1 from the word to the code)
2. **SFE** (+1 from the word to the code)
3. **DBU** (+1 from the word to the code)
4. **579**
5. **712**
6. **FOOT**
7. mope
8. swan
9. silk
10. **AM** (repeating pattern +0/+1, +0/+1)
11. **XZ** (–1, –1)
12. **JR** (+5, –5)

Section 1 Test 11 (page 14)

1. Simon
2. Shiver
3. Oliver
4. B
5. B
6. 11
7. 16
8. 19 July
9. Sunday
10. Friday
11. Saturday
12. May

Section 1 Test 12 (page 15)

1. B
2. D
3. 9
4. 5.00 p.m./five o'clock/17:00
5. 2
6. 6.35 p.m./twenty-five to seven/18:35
7. 40 minutes
8. 11.00 a.m./eleven o'clock/11:00
9. 8.05 a.m./five past eight/08:05
10. 2.25 p.m./twenty-five past two/14:25
11. 2.15 p.m./quarter past two/14:15
12. 2.00 p.m./two o'clock/14:00

Answers

■ Section 2 Test 1 (page 16)

1. 6
2. 3
3. 4
4. C
5. B
6. April
7. October
8. 10
9. 2.10 p.m./ten past two/14:10
10. 31
11. 22 February
12. 1 hour and a half/90 minutes

■ Section 2 Test 2 (page 17)

1. grasp
2. estimate
3. harm
4. refuse
5. ocean
6. kennel
7. day
8. food
9. smile
10. ugly
11. empty
12. 17

■ Section 2 Test 3 (page 18)

1–4. [score half a point for each correct answer]
A = two wheels
B = four wheels
C = water vehicle
moped = A, yacht = C, scooter = A,
motorbike = A, kayak = C, truck = B,
lorry = B, dinghy = C
5. pink, red (the others are shades of blue)
6. galaxy, sun (the others are planets)
7. feathers, river (the others are birds)
8. wink, grin (the others are grumpy words)
9. sympathetic
10. miniature
11. strawberry
12. 3

■ Section 2 Test 4 (page 19)

1. burglar, dislike (the others are when you are not allowed to do something)
2. cup, jump (the others are all ways to throw)
3. wolf, puppy (the others are big cats)
4. waste, scarf (the others are parts of the body)
5. tadpole
6. walked
7. safe
8. tab
9. clasp, clip
10. miniature, tiny
11. least, minimum
12. D

■ Section 2 Test 5 (page 20)

1. lap, ram
2. thin, swam
3. law, and
4. rain, each
5. LOT (CLOTHES)
6. HUG (HUGE)
7. LIT (POLITE)
8. RIB (HORRIBLE)
9. PALE
10. DEER
11. LOOP
12. Frank

■ Section 2 Test 6 (page 21)

1. hall
2. shine
3. one
4. lion
5. PAIN [VAIN] VEIN
6. LAKE [LIKE] PIKE
7. BIKE [BAKE] RAKE
8. SING [KING] KIND
9. tapeworm
10. stingray
11. lighthouse
12. 35

Section 2 Test 7 (page 22)

1. bean (It could <u>be an</u>yone's book!)
2. them (<u>The m</u>en were so tall.)
3. shot (It is never right to pu<u>sh ot</u>hers.)
4. slam (That is Paul'<u>s lam</u>p.)
5. b (shrub and breath, stub and born)
6. l (pencil and leave, still and level)
7. s (grass and shout, dress and shove)
8. bookcase
9. headteacher
10. anyone
11. motorbike
12. 2

Section 2 Test 8 (page 23)

1. 21 (+4)
2. 96 (×2)
3. 32 (+5)
4. 5 (−6)
5. E (7 × 9 + 8 = 71)
6. C (130 − 25 − 5 = 100)
7. A (3 × 4 × 5 = 60)
8. A (4 × 6 − 7 = 17)
9. 4 (a ÷ b)
10. 11 (a − b)
11. 84 (a × b)
12. a potato

Section 2 Test 9 (page 24)

1. 1
2. 5
3. 1
4. 3
5. 64 (×2)
6. 14 (−4)
7. 31 (−5, −4, −3, −2, −1)
8. 29 (+3, +4, +5, +6, +7)
9. A (36 ÷ 6 + 8 = 14)
10. C (90 + 50 − 30 = 110)
11. E (72 ÷ 8 + 5 = 14)
12. D

Section 2 Test 10 (page 25)

1. 12 (a ÷ b)
2. 60 (a + b)
3. 48 (a × b)
4. 30 (a + b)
5. 2
6. 10
7. 8
8. A (150 − 35 + 40 = 155)
9. B (6 × 9 + 18 = 72)
10. B (160 − 40 + 15 = 135)
11. E (3 × 7 − 10 = 11)
12. A

Section 2 Test 11 (page 26)

1. cape
2. teal
3. road
4. rats
5. 8154
6. 3152
7. FAME
8. RARE
9. AE (+3/−1, +1)
10. ZL (−3/+1, −1)
11. NO (+2, −1)
12. 7

Section 2 Test 12 (page 27)

1. mock
2. peer
3. note
4. CVMM (+1 from the word to the code)
5. PSF (+1 from the word to the code)
6. STAR (−1 from the code to the word)
7. FIX (+1 from the code to the word)
8. OH (−3, −3)
9. SV (−2, −2)
10. KT (+1, +1)
11. OX (−1, −1)
12. 14

Answers

■ Section 3 Test 1 (page 28)

1–4. *[score half a point for each correct answer]*
pupil = S, porter = H, patient = H,
headteacher = S, surgeon = H,
midwife = H, tutor = S, doctor = H

5. **25** (×2, −1)
6. **2** (÷5)
7. **27** (×3)
8. **8** (÷10)
9. starstruck
10. firework
11. battleship
12. 8

■ Section 3 Test 2 (page 29)

1. **14** (a × b)
2. **8** (a ÷ b)
3. **17** (a − b)
4. **3** (a ÷ b)
5. RODE
6. POOL
7. ROPE
8. TIED
9. BIT (HABIT)
10. EAT (CHEAT)
11. CAP (ESCAPE)
12. A

■ Section 3 Test 3 (page 30)

1. night, right
2. pip, kin
3. lace, moth
4. four, sort
5. 3
6. 10
7. 1
8. 2
9. 3965
10. 8219
11. LINE
12. his brother's card

■ Section 3 Test 4 (page 31)

1. snowdrop
2. turn
3. lorry
4. Scotland
5. RK (+4, +4)
6. MR (−4, −4)
7. PX (−2, −2)
8. MU (+5, +5)
9. C (6 × 8 + 110 = 158)
10. E (35 ÷ 5 − 7 = 0)
11. D (5 × 6 + 100 = 130)
12. 16

■ Section 3 Test 5 (page 32)

1. **go you** (Where did you go on holiday?)
2. **chocolate is** (My favourite food is chocolate cake.)
3. **looks sister** (Your sister looks just like you.)
4. **capital the** (London is the capital of England.)
5. l (petal and lamp, bawl and leap)
6. h (branch and heavy, fresh and horse)
7. y (grumpy and yellow, grey and yawn)
8. t (robot and town, grunt and tease)
9. YK (+1, +1)
10. YB (−1, −1)
11. GE (+1, same)
12. Hobbes

■ Section 3 Test 6 (page 33)

1. C (25 ÷ 5 + 6 = 11)
2. A (160 − 45 + 20 = 135)
3. B (6 × 7 − 8 = 34)
4. A (81 ÷ 9 + 40 = 49)
5. SUM (+2 from the code to the word)
6. CUP (+3 from the code to the word)
7. PART (−2 from the code to the word)
8. just, fair
9. terrible, awful
10. rich, wealthy
11. guide, lead
12. 21

Answers

■ **Section 3 Test 7** (page 34)
1. jellyfish
2. something
3. eyeball
4. keyhole
5. m (alarm and mark, doom and make)
6. f (calf and fail, hoof and four)
7. r (sour and round, deer and raise)
8. p (pump and prince, soup and plain)
9. dove (I tripped over the step.)
10. date (The tiger growled at everyone it saw.)
11. this (After the race Alex caught his breath.)
12. 35 minutes

■ **Section 3 Test 8** (page 35)
1. 8 (a ÷ b)
2. 95 (a − b)
3. 100 (a × b)
4. 35 (a + b)
5. freeze, melt
6. first, last
7. multiply, divide
8. asleep, awake
9. SEAM [SEAT] HEAT
10. GOAL [GOAT] BOAT
11. BIKE [BITE] KITE
12. D

■ **Section 3 Test 9** (page 36)
1. rats
2. last
3. dare
4. place
5. meteor
6. observe
7. message
8. amphibian
9. summer
10. mice
11. loop
12. Anuska and Melanie

■ **Section 3 Test 10** (page 37)
1. AU (−4, −4)
2. MM (+3, +3)
3. KF (−5, −5)
4. HT (−2, −2)
5. compliment, explain (the others are to do with moaning)
6. jump, poke (the others are to do with shaking)
7. sunny, glare (the others describe being clever)
8. job, steal (the others are about changing)
9. CH (−4, −4)
10. CJ (+2, +2)
11. BU (−3, −3)
12. 8 (half 28 is 14, minus 6 = 8)

■ **Section 3 Test 11** (page 38)
1. outside
2. cram
3. steal
4. toes
5. 31 (+4, +1)
6. 230 (−40, −30, −20, −10)
7. 25 (−5, +1)
8. flag
9. clot
10. bank
11. cure
12. 22 July

■ **Section 3 Test 12** (page 39)
1. 2
2. 30
3. 8
4. 9
5. 8146
6. 2311
7. GRAPE
8. many, few
9. always, never
10. shrink, grow
11. more, less
12. C

Rapid Reasoning Tests | Schofield & Sims

Verbal Reasoning 3 Answers   A7

This book of answers is a pull-out section from
Rapid Reasoning Tests: Verbal Reasoning 3

Published by Schofield & Sims Ltd,
Dogley Mill, Fenay Bridge, Huddersfield HD8 0NQ, UK
Telephone 01484 607080
www.schofieldandsims.co.uk

Author: **Siân Goodspeed**. Siân Goodspeed has asserted her moral right under the Copyright, Designs and Patents Act, 1988, to be identified as the author of this work.

British Library Cataloguing in Publication Data. A catalogue record for this book is available from the British Library.

Commissioned by **Carolyn Richardson Publishing Services** (www.publiserve.co.uk)

Design by **Oxford Designers & Illustrators**

Printed in India by **Multivista Global Ltd**

ISBN 978 07217 1240 6

Target time: 10 minutes

■ If these words were listed in alphabetical order, which word would come **third**? Write the answer on the line.

Example lot many few load too _____lot_____

1. kitchen bathroom bedroom lounge hall _____
2. twinkle shine sparkle glow flash _____
3. one three eight two eleven _____
4. tiger lion elephant leopard lizard _____

■ Change the first word into the last word. Only change one letter at a time. You must make a new word in the middle. Write the new word on the line.

Example MILK [___MILE___] TILE

5. PAIN [_____] VEIN
6. LAKE [_____] PIKE
7. BIKE [_____] RAKE
8. SING [_____] KIND

■ Underline the two words, **one** from each group, that together make one new word. The word from the first group comes first.

Example (<u>clock</u>, watch, week)   (time, <u>work</u>, stop)   (clockwork)

9. (tape, fix, blue)   (bug, worm, fly)
10. (bite, sting, bee)   (ray, light, cloud)
11. (light, candle, white)   (move, house, circuit)

■ Read the following information. Work out the answer. Write your answer on the line.

12. Alice is **10** years old. Her mother is **3** times as old as Alice. Alice's father is **5** years older than her mother. How old is Alice's father? _____

End of test.

Score:		Time taken:		Target met?	

Find the **four-letter word** hidden across two or more consecutive words in each sentence below. The order of the letters must stay the same. Underline the word and write it on the line.

Example My tea made me ill.   _____team_____

1. It could be anyone's book!   _____

2. The men were so tall.   _____

3. It is never right to push others.   _____

4. That is Paul's lamp.   _____

Find the missing letter that completes **both** pairs of words. Write the letter on the lines. Choose your answer from the following letters: **l p b s n t**

Example kil [_t_] oll   ten [_t_] old   (kilt and toll, tent and told)

5. shru [__] reath   stu [__] orn

6. penci [__] eave   stil [__] evel

7. gras [__] hout   dres [__] hove

Underline the two words, **one** from each group, that together make one new word. The word from the first group comes first.

Example (clock, watch, week)   (time, work, stop)   (clockwork)

8. (volume, book, cartoon)   (case, stack, shed)

9. (head, body, mind)   (mother, teacher, man)

10. (any, this, two)   (ship, one, me)

11. (motor, engine, power)   (bus, run, bike)

Read the following information. Work out the answer. Write your answer on the line.

12. Jack has a pet dog. Katie has 2 cats. Joan has a cat, 2 dogs and a fish. How many people have a pet dog?   _____

End of test.

Score:		Time taken:		Target met?	

Target time: 10 minutes

■ Find the next number in the sequence. Write it on the line.

Example 6   9   12   15   18   __21__   (+3 each time)

1. 1   5   9   13   17   __42__
2. 3   6   12   24   48   __9__
3. 7   12   17   22   27   _____
4. 35   29   23   17   11   _____

■ Use the information given to answer the sum. Write your answer as a **letter**.

Example A = 1   B = 2   C = 3   D = 5   E = 8   **A + B + D =** __E__   (1 + 2 + 5 = 8)

5. A = 75   B = 8   C = 9   D = 7   E = 71   **D × C + B =** __62__

6. A = 110   B = 25   C = 100   D = 5   E = 130   **E − B − D =** __100__

7. A = 60   B = 35   C = 3   D = 5   E = 4   **C × E × D =** __60__

8. A = 17   B = 23   C = 7   D = 4   E = 6   **D × E − C =** __17__

(handwritten working to the right: 130 − 25 = 105)

■ Work out the missing number. Write it on the line.

Example 3 [9] 3   4 [8] 2   5 [__15__] 3
(a × b = ?, where a represents the number on the left and b represents the number on the right)

9. 15 [5] 3   28 [7] 4   16 [_____] 4
10. 26 [16] 10   18 [9] 9   17 [_____] 6
11. 5 [35] 7   4 [36] 9   21 [_____] 4

■ Read the following information. Work out the answer. Write your answer on the line.

12. Danyaal is making soup. He puts carrots in and then some celery. After he puts in the celery he adds a potato. He puts salt and pepper in last. What does Danyaal put into the soup third?

_____

End of test.

Score:		Time taken:		Target met?	

Target time: **10 minutes**

Find the missing number in each equation. Write it on the line.

Example 10 – 3 = 2 + ___5___   (10 – 3 = 7 and so does 2 + 5)

1. 27 – 7 = 21 – __1__

2. 17 + 8 = 5 × _____

3. 14 – 3 = 12 – _____

4. 12 + 1 = 10 + _____

Find the missing number in the sequence. Write it on the line.

Example 6   9   12   15   18   ___21___   (+3 each time)

5. 2   4   8   16   32   _____

6. 34   30   26   22   18   _____

7. 45   40   36   33   _____   30

8. 11   14   18   23   _____   36

Use the information given to answer the sum. Write your answer as a **letter**.

Example A = 1   B = 2   C = 3   D = 5   E = 8   **A + B + D =** ___E___   (1 + 2 + 5 = 8)

9. A = 14   B = 36   C = 6   D = 8   E = 17   **B ÷ C + D =** _A_

10. A = 120   B = 30   C = 110   D = 50   E = 90   **E + D – B =** _C_

11. A = 85   B = 72   C = 5   D = 8   E = 14   **B ÷ D + C =** _E_

Circle the letter next to the **true** statement.

12. Every day Jenny is only allowed to listen to the radio after she has taken her dog for a walk. Jenny is listening to the radio now.

If the above statements are true, which one of the following statements must also be true?

A. Jenny's dog is a poodle.

B. Jenny's dog barks at the radio.

C. Jenny is tired after her walk.

D. Jenny has already walked her dog today.

End of test.

Score: _____   Time taken: _____   Target met? _____

Target time: 10 minutes

■ Work out the missing number. Write it on the line.

> **Example** 3 [9] 3   4 [8] 2   5 [___15___] 3
> (a × b = ?, where a represents the number on the left and b represents the number on the right)

1. 60 [5] 12   24 [2] 12   36 [_____] 3
2. 7 [11] 4   24 [31] 7   49 [_____] 11
3. 4 [12] 3   4 [28] 7   4 [_____] 12
4. 22 [46] 24   18 [20] 2   24 [_____] 6

■ Find the missing number in each equation. Write it on the line.

> **Example** 10 – 3 = 2 + ___5___   (10 – 3 = 7 and so does 2 + 5)

5. 20 ÷ 10 = 4 ÷ _____
6. 36 ÷ 2 = 28 – _____
7. 84 – 4 = 10 × _____

■ Use the information given to answer the sum. Write your answer as a **letter**.

> **Example** A = 1   B = 2   C = 3   D = 5   E = 8   **A + B + D =** ___E___   (1 + 2 + 5 = 8)

8. A = 155   B = 40   C = 180   D = 35   E = 150   **E – D + B =** _A_
9. A = 18   B = 72   C = 9   D = 6   E = 81   **D × C + A =** _B_
10. A = 215   B = 135   C = 40   D = 15   E = 160   **E – C + D =** _B_
11. A = 0   B = 10   C = 3   D = 7   E = 11   **C × D – B =** _E_

■ Circle the letter next to the **true** statement.

12. Photographs are pictures made with cameras. Robert is taking a photograph.

If the above statements are true, which one of the following statements must also be true?
A. Robert is using a camera.
B. Cameras have lenses.
C. There are batteries in cameras.
D. Photographs are colourful.

End of test.

Score:		Time taken:		Target met?	

↓ Make a new word by changing the third pair in the same way as the other pairs. Write the new word on the line.

> **Example** (snip, nip) (slit, lit) (then, ___hen___) (take away the first letter of the first word)

1. (elope, pole)   (trace, care)   (space, _____)
2. (robot, boot)   (mince, nice)   (metal, _____)
3. (lance, cane)   (dance, cane)   (board, _____)
4. (timed, emit)   (steps, pets)   (start, _____)

■ Match the number codes to the words. Use this to help you work out the answers to the questions. Write your answers on the lines.

FEET   TREE   WEAK   TEAM   3114   7156   4211   4158

5. What is the code for **MEAT**? _____
6. What is the code for **FEAR**? _____
7. What does the code **3581** mean? _____
8. What does the code **2521** mean? _____

■ Find the missing letter pair in the sequence. Use the alphabet to help you. Write your answer on the line.

A B C D E F G H I J K L M N O P Q R S T U V W X Y Z

> **Example** AD   BE   CF   DG   EH   __FI__   (+1, +1)

9. WA   ZB   YC   BD   _____
10. DP   AO   BN   YM   _____
11. HR   JQ   LP   _____   PN

■ Read the following information. Work out the answer. Write your answer on the line.

12. Fred, Pasqual and Jeff all have a packed lunch. Fred has an apple, a banana and a cheese roll. Pasqual has a ham sandwich and **3** plums. Jeff has a banana, a pear and a biscuit. How many pieces of fruit do they have between them? _____

End of test

Score:	Time taken:	Target met?

↓
The word in square brackets has been made by some of the letters from the two outside words. Make a new word in the middle of the second group of words in the same way. Write the new word on the line.

Example (each [east] slot)   (half [_____hare_____] rope)

1. (fish [hawk] weak)   (beam [_____] cook)
2. (song [sink] like)   (poet [_____] here)
3. (pout [soul] last)   (lots [_____] eons)

Crack the code. Use the alphabet to help you. Write your answer on the line.
A B C D E F G H I J K L M N O P Q R S T U V W X Y Z

Example If the code for **SING** is **TJOH**, what is the code for **LONG**?   MPOH
(+1 from the word to the code each time)

4. If **LOOK** is written in code as **MPPL**, what is the code for **BULL**? _____
5. If **WITH** is written in code as **XJUI**, what is the code for **ORE**? _____
6. If the code for **SUN** is **TVO**, what does the code **TUBS** mean? _____
7. If the code for **MIX** is **LHW**, what does the code **EHW** mean? _____

Find the letter pair that completes each sentence. Use the alphabet to help you. Write your answer on the line.
A B C D E F G H I J K L M N O P Q R S T U V W X Y Z

Example **FP** is to **JT** as **AA** is to ___EE___.   (+4, +4)

8. **IE** is to **FB** as **RK** is to _____.
9. **KO** is to **IM** as **UX** is to _____.
10. **VY** is to **WZ** as **JS** is to _____.
11. **BH** is to **AG** as **PY** is to _____.

Read the following information. Work out the answer. Write your answer on the line.

12. There are 17 people travelling on a train. At the first stop, 3 people leave the train and 2 people get on. At the next stop, 6 people get off and 4 get on. How many people are now travelling on the train? _____

End of test.

1–4. Look at the groups. For each of the words below, choose the correct group. Write its letter on the line.

H = hospital   **S** = school

pupil _____   porter _____   patient _____

headteacher _____   surgeon _____

midwife _____   tutor _____   doctor _____

Find the missing number in the sequence. Write it on the line.

Example 6   9   12   15   18   _21_   (+3 each time)

5. 7   14   13   26   _____   50
6. 250   50   10   _____   0.4
7. 1   3   9   _____   81
8. 8000   800   80   _____   0.8

Underline the two words, **one** from each group, that together make one new word. The word from the first group comes first.

Example (<u>clock</u>, watch, week)   (time, <u>work</u>, stop)   (clockwork)

9. (star, sun, planet)   (hit, struck, band)
10. (fire, burn, match)   (job, office, work)
11. (bar, battle, fight)   (boat, ship, water)

Read the following information. Work out the answer. Write your answer on the line.

12. Five children are called Mia, Michael, Hannah, Amelia and Maria. How many times altogether does the letter 'a' appear among their names? _____

End of test

Score:		Time taken:		Target met?	

Target time: **10 minutes**

■ Work out the missing number. Write it on the line.

> **Example** 3 [9] 3   4 [8] 2   5 [_15_] 3
>
> (a × b = ?, where a represents the number on the left and b represents the number on the right)

1. 2 [24] 12   2 [16] 8   2 [_____] 7
2. 9 [3] 3   15 [5] 3   24 [_____] 3
3. 80 [70] 10   79 [67] 12   100 [_____] 83
4. 36 [12] 3   15 [5] 3   9 [_____] 3

■ Rearrange the letters in capitals to make a new word so that the sentence makes sense. Write the new word on the line.

> **Example** It was **KRDA** outside. ___DARK___

5. Jim **EDOR** his bike to the park. _____
6. The children went swimming in the **POLO**. _____
7. The boat was tied up with a **OPRE**. _____
8. The boy **ETID** his shoelaces. _____

■ In each of the sentences below, the word in capitals has three letters missing. Those three letters spell a word. Write the three-letter word in the gap.

> **Example** I helped my sister tie up her shoe L _A_ _C_ _E_ S.

9. Biting your nails is a bad HA __ __ __.
10. The teacher told the class not to CH __ __ __ on the test.
11. They made a quick ES __ __ __ E.

■ Circle the letter next to the **true** statement.

12. Burrowing animals make warrens to live in. Rabbits are burrowing animals.

If the above statements are true, which one of the following statements must also be true?
A. Rabbits live in warrens.
B. Rabbits are furry and cute.
C. Baby rabbits are called kittens.
D. Foxes chase rabbits down holes.

End of test.

Score:	Time taken:	Target met?

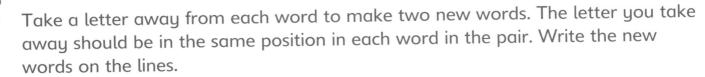

Take a letter away from each word to make two new words. The letter you take away should be in the same position in each word in the pair. Write the new words on the lines.

| **Example** tray, cram | _____ray_____ , _____ram_____ | (remove the first letter from each word) |

1. knight, bright   _____ , _____
2. pipe, king   _____ , _____
3. lance, mouth   _____ , _____
4. flour, snort   _____ , _____

Find the missing number in each equation. Write it on the line.

| **Example** $10 - 3 = 2 +$ ___5___ | $(10 - 3 = 7$ and so does $2 + 5)$ |

5. $21 \div 7 = 9 \div$ __3__
6. $17 + 3 = 2 \times$ __10__
7. $20 \div 10 = 1 +$ __1__
8. $24 + 2 = 28 -$ __2__

Match the number codes to the words. Use this to help you work out the answers to the questions. Write your answers on the lines.

RAIN   REAL   NEAR   ROOT   9217   7139   7556   7218

9. What is the code for **INTO**? _____
10. What is the code for **LEAN**? _____
11. What does the code **8392** mean? _____

Read the following information. Work out the answer. Write your answer on the line.

12. Greg is delivering invitation cards to his mother, brother, sister and father. He posts his card to his mother third, before he posts his card to his father. He posts his sister's card second. Whose card does he post first? __his Farthers__

End of test.

Target time: 10 minutes

■ If these words were listed in alphabetical order, which word would come **fourth**? Write the answer on the line.

| **Example** lot   many   few   load   too | _many_ |

1. bluebell   snowdrop   lily   sunflower   lavender _____
2. spin   turn   dizzy   round   twist _____
3. car   boat   lorry   bicycle   motorbike _____
4. Ireland   Scotland   England   Spain   India _____

■ Find the letter pair that completes each sentence. Use the alphabet to help you. Write your answer on the line.

A B C D E F G H I J K L M N O P Q R S T U V W X Y Z

| **Example** **FP** is to **JT** as **AA** is to __EE__. | (+4, +4) |

5. **SR** is to **WV** as **NG** is to _____.
6. **VH** is to **RD** as **QV** is to _____.
7. **LC** is to **JA** as **RZ** is to _____.
8. **UM** is to **ZR** as **HP** is to _____.

■ Use the information given to answer the sum. Write your answer as a **letter**.

| **Example** A = 1   B = 2   C = 3   D = 5   E = 8   **A + B + D =** __E__ | (1 + 2 + 5 = 8) |

9. A = 110   B = 200   C = 158   D = 6   E = 8   **D × E + A =** _158_
10. A = 35   B = 7   C = 6   D = 5   E = 0   **A ÷ D – B =** _0̶_   7
11. A = 90   B = 5   C = 100   D = 130   E = 6   **B × E + C =** _130_

■ Read the following information. Work out the answer. Write your answer on the line.

12. Shazia is 9 years old. Her sister is 5 years younger than her. Her brother is 4 times as old as Shazia's sister. How old is Shazia's brother? _20_

End of test.

| Score: | | Time taken: | | Target met? | |

Two words in each sentence must change places so that the sentence makes sense. Underline the two words.

Example I am <u>sleepy</u> <u>not</u> yet.   (I am <u>not</u> <u>sleepy</u> yet.)

1. Where did go you on holiday?
2. My favourite food chocolate is cake.
3. Your looks sister just like you.
4. London is capital the of England.

Find the missing letter that completes **both** pairs of words. Write the letter on the lines. Choose your answer from the following letters: **h t l y d r**

Example kil [_t_] oll   ten [_t_] old   (kilt and toll, tent and told)

5. peta [__] amp   baw [__] eap
6. branc [__] eavy   fres [__] orse
7. grump [__] ellow   gre [__] awn
8. robo [__] own   grun [__] ease

Find the missing letter pair in the sequence. Use the alphabet to help you. Write your answer on the line.

A B C D E F G H I J K L M N O P Q R S T U V W X Y Z

Example AD   BE   CF   DG   EH   _FI_   (+1, +1)

9. XJ _____ ZL AM BN
10. AD ZC _____ XA WZ
11. FE _____ HE IE JE

Read the following information. Work out the answer. Write your answer on the line.

12. Four greyhounds are racing. Tawny is two places behind Spangle. Hobbes is in front of Spangle. Shep is two places behind Hobbes. Who is winning the race? _____

End of test.

Target time: 10 minutes

■ Use the information given to answer the sum. Write your answer as a **letter**.

Example A = 1   B = 2   C = 3   D = 5   E = 8   **A + B + D =** ___E___   (1 + 2 + 5 = 8)

1. A = 25   B = 6   C = 11   D = 5   E = 36   **A ÷ D + B =** ~~E~~ 11

2. A = 135   B = 45   C = 160   D = 180   E = 20   **C – B + E =** ~~E~~ 135

3. A = 8   B = 34   C = 42   D = 7   E = 6   **E × D – A =** 34

4. A = 49   B = 81   C = 9   D = 40   E = 54   **B ÷ C + D =** ~~|~~

$$\frac{34\ 2}{8}$$

$$3\ 4$$

■ Crack the code. Use the alphabet to help you. Write your answer on the line.

A B C D E F G H I J K L M N O P Q R S T U V W X Y Z

Example If the code for **SING** is **TJOH**, what is the code for **LONG**? ___MPOH___

(+1 from the word to the code each time)

5. If the code for **PAY** is **NYW**, what does the code **QSK** mean? ~~QSK~~

6. If **GLASS** is written in code as **DIXPP**, what does the code **ZRM** mean? _____

7. If **EACH** is written in code as **GCEJ**, what does the code **RCTV** mean? _____

■ Underline the pair of words that mean almost the **same**.

Example (oven, pan)   (eat, cupboard)   (<u>cook, chef</u>)

8. (travel, bus)   (just, fair)   (circus, coin)

9. (tremble, scary)   (tangle, great)   (terrible, awful)

10. (rich, wealthy)   (collect, sell)   (treasure, silver)

11. (trail, map)   (collar, scout)   (guide, lead)

■ Read the following information. Work out the answer. Write your answer on the line.

12. A flower shop sells Sophie 12 roses, Emil 6 tulips and Amy 3 daffodils. How many flowers does the shop sell to the children altogether? _____

End of test.

Score:	Time taken:	Target met?

Underline the two words, **one** from each group, that together make one new word. The word from the first group comes first.

Example (<u>clock</u>, watch, week)   (time, <u>work</u>, stop)   (clockwork)

1. (pudding, jelly, sweet)   (lizard, fish, swim)
2. (all, some, many)   (it, thing, just)
3. (eye, nose, mouth)   (hair, jug, ball)
4. (lock, door, key)   (turn, wide, hole)

Find the missing letter that completes **both** pairs of words. Write the letter on the lines. Choose your answer from the following letters: **r f m p v t**

Example kil [t] oll   ten [t] old   (kilt and toll, tent and told)

5. alar [__] ark   doo [__] ake
6. cal [__] ail   hoo [__] our
7. sou [__] ound   dee [__] aise
8. pum [__] rince   sou [__] lain

Find the **four-letter word** hidden across two or more consecutive words in each sentence below. The order of the letters must stay the same. Underline the word and write it on the line.

Example My <u>tea m</u>ade me ill.   ___team___

9. I tripped over the step.   _____
10. The tiger growled at everyone it saw.   _____
11. After the race Alex caught his breath.   _____

Read the following information. Work out the answer. Write your answer on the line.

12. Sham is making a cake. He puts the cake in the oven at 9.10 a.m. He takes the cake out of the oven at 9.45 a.m. How many minutes did Sham bake his cake for?   _____

End of test

Score:		Time taken:		Target met?	

Target time: **10 minutes**

■ Work out the missing number. Write it on the line.

Example 3 [9] 3   4 [8] 2   5 [__15__] 3
(a × b = ?, where a represents the number on the left and b represents the number on the right)

1. 54 [9] 6   56 [8] 7   48 [_____] 6
2. 150 [130] 20   90 [70] 20   110 [_____] 15
3. 8 [64] 8   7 [49] 7   10 [_____] 10
4. 19 [27] 8   12 [30] 18   26 [_____] 9

■ Underline the two words, **one** from each group, that are most **opposite** in meaning.

Example (<u>useless</u>, broken, mend)   (<u>useful</u>, fix, tool)

5. (chill, store, freeze)   (cook, melt, keep)
6. (first, one, won)   (second, last, show)
7. (sum, multiply, time)   (divide, some, mix)
8. (dream, pause, asleep)   (wait, lively, awake)

■ Change the first word into the last word. Only change one letter at a time. You must make a new word in the middle. Write the new word on the line.

Example MILK [__MILE__] TILE

9. SEAM [_____] HEAT
0. GOAL [_____] BOAT
1. BIKE [_____] KITE

■ Circle the letter next to the **true** statement.

2. Cutlery is used to eat food. A spoon is a type of cutlery.

If the above statements are true, which one of the following statements must also be true?
A. Tablecloths are useful to keep the table clean.
B. Knives are used for cutting food.
C. People use cutlery to put their cups on.
D. Spoons are used to eat food.

End of test.

Score:		Time taken:		Target met?	

⬇
◼ Make a new word by changing the third pair in the same way as the other pairs. Write the new word on the line.

> **Example** (snip, nip) (slit, lit) (then, ___hen___) (take away the first letter of the first word)

1. (swaps, wasp)   (swipe, wisp)   (trash, _____)
2. (swine, wise)   (ships, hiss)   (slant, _____)
3. (brain, barn)   (drain, darn)   (drape, _____)

◼ Underline the word that goes best with the three words in brackets.

> **Example** (fork, teaspoon, knife)   plate, glass, <u>spoon</u>

4. (space, area, spot)   place, see, rocket
5. (star, planet, sun)   son, meteor, square
6. (watch, view, gaze)   observe, clock, listen
7. (mail, post, letter)   man, plank, message

◼ Choose the word that best completes the sentence. Underline the answer.

> **Example** **Snow** is to **cold** as **sunshine** is to (sky, <u>hot</u>, cloud).

8. **Fly** is to **insect** as **frog** is to (mammal, green, amphibian, pond).
9. **Fat** is to **thin** as **winter** is to (summer, spring, autumn, snow).
10. **Leaf** is to **leaves** as **mouse** is to (shrimps, mice, kittens, hole).
11. **Hop** is to **hoop** as **lop** is to (loop, swoop, moot, mop).

◼ Read the following information. Work out the answer. Write your answer on the lines.

12. Anuska goes to the gym on Mondays and Thursdays. Pete goes to the gym on Tuesdays, Wednesday and Fridays. On Mondays, Thursdays and Fridays Melanie visits the gym. Which two people go to the gym on a Thursday? _____ and _____

End of tes

Score:		Time taken:		Target met?	

Target time: 10 minutes

Find the letter pair that completes each sentence. Use the alphabet to help you. Write your answer on the line.

A B C D E F G H I J K L M N O P Q R S T U V W X Y Z

> **Example** **FP** is to **JT** as **AA** is to __EE__.   (+4, +4)

1. **VN** is to **RJ** as **EY** is to _____.
2. **MR** is to **PU** as **JJ** is to _____.
3. **SW** is to **NR** as **PK** is to _____.
4. **FN** is to **DL** as **JV** is to _____.

In each group, three words go together. Two words do not go with the other three. Underline the **two** words that are the **odd ones out**.

> **Example** great   excellent   <u>awful</u>   brilliant   <u>terrible</u>

5. moan   complain   compliment   grumble   explain
6. shake   shudder   jump   shiver   poke
7. bright   clever   sunny   smart   glare
8. swap   exchange   job   steal   switch

Find the missing letter pair in the sequence. Use the alphabet to help you. Write your answer on the line.

A B C D E F G H I J K L M N O P Q R S T U V W X Y Z

> **Example** AD   BE   CF   DG   EH   __FI__   (+1, +1)

9. GL   _____   YD   UZ   QV
10. WD   YF   AH   _____   EL
11. HA   EX   _____   YR   VO

Read the following information. Work out the answer. Write your answer on the line.

12. Shana thinks of a number. She adds 6 to her number. She then doubles the answer she gets. She gets the new answer **28**. What number was Shana first thinking of? _____

End of test.

Score:		Time taken:		Target met?	

■ Choose the word that best completes the sentence. Underline the answer.

> **Example** **Snow** is to **cold** as **sunshine** is to (sky, <u>hot</u>, cloud).

1. **Swift** is to **slow** as **inside** is to (garden, outside, house, box).
2. **Clamp** is to **clam** as **cramp** is to (ramp, sore, cram, tent).
3. **Buy** is to **purchase** as **rob** is to (boy, steal, name, steel).
4. **Hand** is to **fingers** as **foot** is to (shoe, sock, toes, kick).

■ Find the missing number in the sequence. Write it on the line.

> **Example** 6   9   12   15   18   __21__   (+3 each time)

5. 17   21   22   26   27   __31__
6. 320   280   250   __230__   220
7. 38   33   34   29   30   _____

■ The word in square brackets has been made by some of the letters from the two outside words. Make a new word in the middle of the second group of words in the same way. Write the new word on the line.

> **Example** (each [east] slot)   (ha<u>lf</u> [___hare___] <u>r</u>ope)

8. (evil [ergo] glory)   (fork [_____] angle)
9. (bark [brat] tone)   (cold [_____] tame)
10. (marry [mane] nosey)   (balmy [_____] necks)
11. (drake [date] troll)   (chute [_____] raise)

■ Read the following information. Work out the answer. Write your answer on the line.

12. Troy's school breaks up for the summer in 13 days. If it is 9 July today, what date does his school break up? _____

End of test

Score:	Time taken:	Target met?

Target time: 10 minutes

■ Find the missing number in each equation. Write it on the line.

Example 10 – 3 = 2 + ___5___   (10 – 3 = 7 and so does 2 + 5)

1. 30 – 15 = 30 ÷ _____
2. 86 – 7 = 109 – _____
3. 5 × 6 = 22 + _____
4. 29 + 8 = 46 – _____

■ Match the number codes to the words. Use this to help you work out the answers to the questions. Write your answers on the lines.

LEAP   PAGE   LEAN   RIPE   8421   3148   6581   3147

5. What is the code for **PEAR**? _____
6. What is the code for **GLEE**? _____
7. What does the code **26481** mean? _____

■ Underline the pair of words that are most **opposite** in meaning.

Example (useful, useless)   (fix, mend)   (broken, tool)

8. (lot, meek)   (many, few)   (too, also)
9. (always, never)   (very, two)   (once, then)
10. (trace, slip)   (small, flower)   (shrink, grow)
11. (any, plenty)   (more, less)   (grip, let)

■ Circle the letter next to the **true** statement.

12. Animals that are active during the night are nocturnal. Owls are nocturnal.

If the above statements are true, which one of the following statements must also be true?
A. Owls hunt mice.
B. There are lots of different types of owl.
C. Owls are active at night-time.
D. It is fun to be awake at night.

End of test.

Score:	Time taken:	Target met?

Schofield&Sims

the long-established educational publisher specialising in maths, English and science

Verbal Reasoning 3 is a collection of short, language-based problem solving tests. Each timed test includes age-appropriate questions, providing opportunities for children to practise and master verbal reasoning skills in preparation for the 11+ and other school selection tests. This book is part of the **Rapid Reasoning Tests** series and covers the following question types: word and letter patterns; vocabulary; spelling; number patterns and problem solving.

Rapid Reasoning Tests provides short, effective, timed tests in reasoning. The series comprises six books of verbal reasoning tests and six books of non-verbal reasoning tests.

Written by experienced teachers and designed for independent use, **Rapid Reasoning Tests** has been carefully structured to provide practice of key, standard format question types. Each collection of tests has been designed for use over one year and provides one section per term in order to support regular practice.

Key features

- **Short tests** requiring few resources that are easy to fit into a busy timetable.
- A **target time** for each test encourages children to work quickly and develop the necessary exam skills for success in the 11+ and other tests.
- **Pull-out answers** in the centre of each book can be easily removed.
- **Free downloads** to support the series are available from the Schofield & Sims website.

The full series includes the following books:

Verbal Reasoning 1 978 07217 1238 3	**Non-verbal Reasoning 1** 978 07217 1226 0	**(Ages 6–7)**
Verbal Reasoning 2 978 07217 1239 0	**Non-verbal Reasoning 2** 978 07217 1227 7	**(Ages 7–8)**
Verbal Reasoning 3 978 07217 1240 6	**Non-verbal Reasoning 3** 978 07217 1228 4	**(Ages 8–9)**
Verbal Reasoning 4 978 07217 1241 3	**Non-verbal Reasoning 4** 978 07217 1229 1	**(Ages 9–10)**
Verbal Reasoning 5 978 07217 1242 0	**Non-verbal Reasoning 5** 978 07217 1230 7	**(Ages 10–11)**
Verbal Reasoning 6 978 07217 1243 7	**Non-verbal Reasoning 6** 978 07217 1231 4	**(Ages 11–12)**

MIX
Paper from responsible sources
FSC® C110589

ISBN 978-0721-71313-7

9 780721 713137

ISBN 978 07217 1240 6

Key Stage 2

Age range 8–9

£3.95

(Retail price)

For further information and to place an order visit
www.schofieldandsims.co.uk or telephone 01484 607080